Dodd, Mead Wonderland Books

The Everglades: Florida Wonderland
Greece: Wonderland of the Past and Present
Hawaii: Pacific Wonderland
Southwest Desert Wonderland
Spain: Wonderland of Contrasts

Southwest Desert Wonderland

By

Norman Hammond Wakeman

Illustrated with photographs by the author

DODD, MEAD & COMPANY

New York

For my children—Bill, Jim and Caroline

Frontispiece: *Saguaros are cacti that live only where there are cloudbursts to supply their water needs. During the summer months warm moist air from the Gulf of California moves northward across southwestern Arizona. The hot desert sand and rock causes hot rising air. The result, cloudbursts. The roots of the saguaro quickly gather the water and store it in the stems. A large saguaro may take in a ton of water after such a cloudburst. During the dry months that follow the plant uses so much of the water that the stems shrink forming the wrinkles or pleats.*

Contents

1. An Introduction to the Southwest Desert Wonderland   7

2. The Desert   9

    Tropical Deserts   10
    Topographic Deserts   11
    Salty Alkaline Lakes   14
    Deserts Are Hot   17
    Deserts Have Extremes of Temperature   18
    Mirages   18
    Deserts Are Windy   19
    Desert Soil   22
    Sand Dunes   23

3. History of the Desert   25

    Geology and Paleontology   25
    Anthropology of the Desert   29

4. Plant Adaptations   32

    Lichens   32
    Trees and Shrubs   33
    Annuals   44

5. Animal Adaptations   46

    Index   63

The Colorado Desert of Southern California as seen from the ten thousand-foot summit of Mt. San Jacinto.

I

An Introduction to the Southwest Desert Wonderland

Semi-arid Southern California has always been the home of Norman Wakeman and his family, where Mr. Wakeman has been a professor of biology at Pasadena City College for twenty years. At one time, they lived on an island in a harbor at Newport Beach. Now their home is right at the foot of Mount Wilson on whose six-thousand-foot summit is perched the observatory that houses the hundred-inch Carnegie telescope. This is all a part of the towering Coast Range, which, together with the Sierra Nevadas, is almost solely responsible for the *Southwest Desert Wonderland,* lying in the rain shadow of these ten- and fourteen-thousand-foot peaks.

Palm Springs of the Colorado Desert and Las Vegas of the Mojave Desert are just a few hours' drive through the mountain passes for the residents of Southern California, including the Wakemans. Without modern air conditioning, the desert would be almost unlivable during the summer months. However, starting in October and lasting all during the winter and on into the early spring of March and April, except for the cool evenings, the temperature is ideal. The skies are almost always cloudless and very blue. At night, the stars seem brighter than they do any other place on earth. People from all over the world are learning to love the desert. Three hundred thousand visitors from the United States alone come to Palm Springs each winter.

With a little rain in spring, almost every foot of sand and gravel comes into glorious bloom, with more than five hundred species of flowers.

Most desert animals stay under cover by day and come out hunting at night. Anybody driving at night and watching carefully may see kit foxes, coyotes, and bobcats. They may glimpse little kangaroo rats hopping on their long hind legs across the highway, as well as countless reptiles and busy beetles. All of the desert animals must move across the road sooner or later, with the exception of the owls, hawks, and eagles that fly above it.

There are interesting sights in the daytime, too. It is a good idea, first of all, to learn to recognize the tracks that are left on the sand. Quite often, by following these tracks, the animals that made them may be found hiding under the desert shrubs and trees or down in burrows or even under rocks.

Mr. Wakeman writes, "Countless weekends on the desert hunting for animals with the help of students and photographing the animals that we have caught during the night in nets and traps have taught me much. But the greatest inspiration and help I have received have been from joining weekend expeditions to the desert with such capable field biologists as Dr. Raymond Cowles, Emeritus Professor of Zoology, University of California, at Los Angeles, and Dr. Edmund C. Jaeger, formerly of Riverside City College, at Riverside, whose many wonderful books about the desert have been invaluable to me.

"Along with learning has come much adventure. I will always shudder when I think of the time a student was grasping a rattlesnake just below the head and pulling its fangs out with a stick so that the venom would drip off and we could get a photograph. He held himself so motionless for the camera that it made him faint and he fell over backward, still clutching the snake. I had to wait until he regained consciousness before he relaxed his grip enough so that I could take the snake with my bare hands, a new experience for me. Up until then, I had always used a snake hook on the end of a long pole!"

2

The Desert

The word desert used to mean any place deserted by man—icy wastes at the poles and at the tops of mountains, forests, and jungles. Now the word has come to mean just one kind of region in the world—the barren, rocky, sandy, almost rainless places, with great extremes of heat and frequent devastating winds. Deserts are located on both sides of the Tropic of Cancer and the Tropic of Capricorn. Because of the heavy rainfall at the equator, they are not found in that region. Rather, they are associated with what are known as the horse latitudes, between 30 and 40 degrees in both hemispheres, because of the great dryness there. Deserts cover one-tenth of the land surface of the earth and are found on all of the continents except Europe, Greenland, and Antarctica.

The desert is so different from any other region of the world that it has its own plant and animal life. It is misleading to call any other type of land area a desert. If man doesn't know the difference between a desert and Arctic wastes, the plants and animals do. Polar bears of the Arctic have pads of fur on their feet to keep them warm. The desert kit fox has pads of extra-thick skin to keep the bottoms of its feet cool. There seems to be no limit to the extent to which creatures are adapted to their special environments in their fight for survival in all the different regions of the world.

The deserts of the earth receive an average annual rainfall of little more than five inches. The world's driest area is the Atacama Desert, on the west coast of South America, with a recording of two-hundredths of an inch precipitation each year for forty years. Libya and Egypt, in the Sahara Desert of North Africa, average about an inch of rain a year. Only the Nile River makes Egypt fertile. Death

The desert kit fox has long pointed ears that serve as sensitive screens to detect the slightest rustle in the bush. It relies upon great speed to catch its prey.

Valley, located in the Mojave Desert of Southern California, is the most extreme desert of North America, with an annual rainfall of one and a third inches in recent years.

TROPICAL DESERTS

Deserts of the tropics are dry because trade winds originating in the horse latitudes are dry to start with and, as they blow across the land toward the equator, they become warmer. The warmer the air, the more moisture it can hold. What little moisture may be in the land, the trade winds will gather up. The driest and largest deserts in the world are tropical deserts. Examples of these are the Sahara Desert, that covers the northern half of Africa, and its neighbor, the Arabian Desert; most of the Australian deserts; the deserts of northern Mexico, and the Atacama Desert of northern Chile. The trade winds that waft across the Atacama would be moist, since they blow over the Pacific Ocean, except that the cold Humboldt Current flows northward along this coast and cools the trades, so that they are unable to take up much moisture from the sea. Only warm air blowing over the ocean can absorb appreciable quantities of water vapor. When these cool, dry trades reach the land, however, they are warmed and are then able to carry moisture, so, instead of giving rain to the Atacama Desert, these winds dry it out even more.

TOPOGRAPHIC DESERTS

Another reason for dry deserts is to be found in the high mountain ranges that stand between them and the sea. When moist ocean breezes cross a mountain, they are dried. The low atmospheric pressure of high altitudes expands and cools the air, just as air released

The Colorado Desert of Southern California was made by such high mountains as ten thousand foot high Mt. San Jacinto of the Coast Range. What little moisture the Pacific Ocean breezes brought was precipitated as rain and snow on the tops of the mountains.

from a bicycle tire is cooled when it expands. Moisture in the form of rain, hail, and snow falls on the mountain top, leaving very little for the desert beyond. Deserts that are the result of their location relative to the topography of the land and sea are called topographic deserts.

There are topographic deserts on four continents. In eastern Asia there is the Gobi Desert of Mongolia. Not only is this desert too far inland for moist ocean breezes to reach it, but the highest mountains in the world, including Mount Everest, would never permit the drenching rains from the Indian Ocean monsoons to pass. So much of the continent of Asia is covered by deserts and the mountains that made them, there is not enough soil to produce the food needed by the vast population. Two-thirds of the people of the world live in Asia.

It has already been said that, on the continent of Australia, the dry trade winds have made a tropical desert. In addition, the Great Dividing Range, extending all along the east coast of Australia, with Mount Kosciusko one of its soaring peaks, has made a topographic desert here also. Moist southeast trade winds, blowing in from the Pacific Ocean, bring twenty to forty inches of rain to the coastal Australian cities of Melbourne and Sydney during the winter and spring, making this region a wonderful grazing and farming land, but by the time these winds have crossed the mountains, there is very little rain left in them for the desert. Because of these factors, only 1 per cent of Australia, a continent that is nearly as large as the United States, is is under cultivation.

Another topographic desert is found in western Argentina and Patagonia of South America. Moist westerlies bring rain to make the Chilean slopes of the Andes a fertile garden spot, but by the time they have crossed Mount Aconcagua and the Andes, the longest mountain range in the world, there isn't very much left for the other side of the mountain away from the sea.

In North America, the southwestern United States and northern Mexico have a near monopoly on deserts. Except for the deserts of northern Mexico, these are all topographical deserts. They all lie back of mountains, away from the ocean. Mountain ranges that are more extensive than the entire alpine system of Europe extend all along the west coast of the United States and Mexico. There are the Cascades of Oregon and northern California; the Sierra Nevada range, over four hundred miles long, in California; the Coast Range of Southern California and Baja California in Mexico. Each of these ranges has peaks more than ten thousand feet high. The Sierra alone has forty-one peaks over ten thousand and six over fourteen thousand feet high. What chance will rain-filled Pacific Ocean winds, the westerlies, have to cross such formidable mountains as these? Their snow-capped peaks all through the winter and spring, are the telltale evidence of where the moisture left off. The result is the Great Basin Desert, extending from southeastern Oregon across southern Utah and northern Nevada, the Mojave Desert of Southern California, and most of Nevada and northwestern Arizona, and the Colorado Desert

The coati is a relative of the raccoon. Though a native of Central America it is a frequent visitor to the Arizona Desert. Its nose is very long and sensitive to odors and touch. It uses it to investigate almost everything.

of Southern California and southwestern Arizona, merging with the Sonoran Desert of Mexico. The Chihuahua Desert of Mexico, that merges with the deserts of western Texas and southern New Mexico, is a tropical desert, since it is dried by the winds of the horse latitudes, and a topographic desert, since it lies so far from the sea.

SALTY ALKALINE LAKES

Since topographic deserts by nature are either hemmed in by mountains or lie so far within the interior of a continent that they are isolated by distance from the ocean, whatever drainage by stream or river that takes place usually ends up in a lake in the lowest part of the desert. There are five classic examples of this in the southwestern section of the United States. The lowest place in the Western Hemisphere is Bad Water, at Death Valley, a salty alkaline lake, 282 feet below the level of the sea. In addition to being so far below sea level, Mount Whitney, 14,495 feet high, is just one of the impressive peaks that tower above it, making it impossible for water to escape.

Not only is the Great Salt Lake in Utah cut off from possible drainage to the sea by the Wasatch Range to the east, but this is also prevented by hundreds of miles of mile-high desert, plus the Sierra Nevada and Cascade ranges to the west. The Colorado River runs between Nevada and Arizona, in the Mojave Desert, and between California and Arizona, in the Colorado Desert, ending in the Gulf of California, in Mexico. Before the Hoover Dam was built to control the river, from time to time during the flood season in the winter, the river would overflow its banks and run into the lowest place in Imperial Valley in Southern California, which is 241 feet below sea level. Thus was formed the Salton Sea whose name is self-descriptive.

Located just a few miles northeast of mile-high Reno, on the eastern slope of the Sierra Nevada Range in the Great Basin Desert of Nevada, is Pyramid Lake. This salty lake has no outlet, being surrounded by high mountains and high desert. It is fed by overflow waters from Lake Tahoe in the Sierra, by way of the Truckee River that flows through Reno. About a hundred miles south in the same

14

Bad Water, Death Valley, in the Mojave Desert of California is a big sink at the bottom of America. It is the lowest place in the Western Hemisphere. Telescope Peak of the Panamint Mountains towers over eleven thousand feet above the valley. Mt. Whitney of the Sierra is a few miles beyond.

desert, but in California, is Mono Lake, another saline lake, situated on the east slope of the Sierra and isolated from the sea for the same reason as Pyramid Lake.

In addition to the few lakes that contain salty mineral-filled water, there are countless numbers of dry lake beds which are all that remains after the water has evaporated off or sunk into the soil. Most of these lake beds are as level and flat as the water surface that preceded them. The home of the great experimental rocket ship, the *X-15*, known as Edwards Air Force Base, is Muroc Dry Lake. It is located in the Mojave Desert of California, on the eastern slope of the Coast Range of Southern California, between the towns of Mojave and Palmdale.

Practically everyone has heard of Bonneville Lake, near Great Salt Lake. This huge dry lake bed is so even and flat and has such a hard covering of mineral, known as a salt pan, that it is a favorite proving ground for high-speed automobiles.

15

A chemical analysis of the minerals that are leached out of the soil and deposited in these desert lakes shows that they are 95 per cent compounds, composed of sodium and chlorine (which is table salt), magnesium and sulfur (which forms magnesium sulfate or epsom salts, an emetic—a reason for not drinking the water), potassium and calcium in the form of lime. The remaining 5 per cent can be almost every other element, but especially boron, a nonmetallic element that occurs only in combination, as with sodium and oxygen in borax. The famous mule teams of Death Valley hauled tons of this mineral, which has great commercial value in making glass, pottery, enamels, and soaps. It is also used to prepare boric acid and water softeners. Next in abundance is strontium, then silicon and iron. The latter becomes evident when it oxidizes to form different shades of rusty red.

When sea water is analyzed as to the quantity and quality of minerals it contains, the percentage composition is found to be nearly identical to that of the desert salt lakes. This illustrates quite well

Ocotillo has scarlet tubular flowers that are so numerous on the stems that they seem to be aflame with color. The ground is covered with a flower called goldfields.

how the rivers and streams that bring minerals to the desert lakes carry the same minerals as those that go to the sea.

The sun shines on the deserts more than on any other areas in the world because of the moisture-free skies above them and their nearness to the equator, the only place where the sun ever shines directly overhead. This means that the sun is more nearly overhead at the latitudes of the deserts than it is at any other place except the equator. The combination of a cloudless sky and nearly direct overhead rays from the sun makes for a very hot place. The two hottest places on earth are Death Valley, in the Mojave Desert of Southern California with a temperature record of 135°F., and the Libyan Desert, a part of the Sahara of North Africa, with a record of 136°F.

These are not the only reasons that deserts are hot. Since deserts are covered with rock, gravel, and sand, which require very little heat to cause a temperature change, their temperatures rise rapidly. Physicists describe such materials as having a low heat capacity. Water has the highest heat capacity of anything on earth, which means that it requires more heat to change the temperature of water than it does to change the temperature of any other substance. That is why water is used to keep our automobiles running cool. Aviators know that where there is a bare rock, there may be an updraft of hot air, but where there is a body of water, there may be a downdraft of relatively cool air, yet the water has been exposed to the same rays of the sun as the rock. Besides, the rock is a good conductor of heat and the water is a very poor conductor. This means that the rock will give heat to the air quickly and the water will give heat very slowly. Aviators also know that where there are many plants growing, there tends to be a cooling of the air and a downdraft such as is found over water.

Protoplasm is the substance out of which all living things are made. Since about three-fourths of its weight is water, it has approximately the same heat capacity and conductivity as water. Because of the scarcity of water and plants and the great abundance of rock, gravel, and sand in deserts, we have a third reason why they are hot.

DESERTS HAVE EXTREMES OF TEMPERATURE

Since rock, gravel, and sand have a low heat capacity but are good conductors of heat, they not only heat up rapidly during the sunshine hours and warm the air, they also cool down rapidly at night and reduce the temperature of the air. Plants with their water content retain heat for long periods of time. Temperature changes take place very slowly near the ocean. But on the desert it is quite different. The Syrian Desert of the Sahara has the record for the greatest temperature variation in a twenty-four-hour period. In January 1936, the temperature rose to 110°F. in the daytime and dropped below freezing, to 20°F, at night, a variation of 90°. In the deserts of southwestern United States, Death Valley, California, records average variations of forty degrees between daytime and nighttime. Palm Springs, California, and Las Vegas, Nevada, average about the same range. The temperature changes can never be so abrupt in these desert areas as they are in the interior regions of the Sahara, however, because the nearby Pacific Ocean, with its high heat capacity, helps to moderate the temperature variation.

MIRAGES

Desert heat causes mirages. Many a thirsty desert traveler has seen in the distance what appeared to be lifesaving water, only to discover that there was really none at all. What was seen was a patch of blue sky that looked as though it were on the ground, instead of up where

Bigelow's cholla is the most treacherous of the spiny cacti of the desert. The spines are sharp and barbed so that once they have pierced the flesh they tend to stay put and are painful to extract. What a wonderful protection against predators are these spines for the cactus wren and the roadrunner that build their nests among the forbidding branches of the cholla.

The barrel-like stem of the barrel cactus may grow to a height of eight feet. The pulpy stem material is wringing wet with water to drink.

it belonged. Whenever light rays pass from material of one density to another, they are bent. This is the principle of optics and it explains why lenses bend and focus light rays. A wooden stick held by one end while the other is dipped into water appears to be bent because the light rays coming from the dense water to the less dense air are bent. When light rays from the sky go from relatively less dense warm air above the desert into superheated air on the ground, they are bent from the ground upward toward the observer, who immediately thinks the blue color is coming from the ground and that it could only be water because that is the thought and desire uppermost in his mind.

Sometimes things on the ground, such as palm trees, look as though they are up in the sky. This happens when the relatively cooler, denser air is down low and the less dense, warmer air is high up. Rays of light from the palm trees that go upward toward the sky are bent downward toward the observer, so that a mirage of trees is seen in the sky. When the cooler air is near the ground, it is usually because there is water there to cool it. This type of mirage in the sky could lead a person to water and save a life because where there are palm trees, there is apt to be a desert spring—an oasis.

DESERTS ARE WINDY

The winds for which the deserts are noted are caused by extremes of temperature. The light, hot air rises thousands of feet into the sky in the daytime and falls rapidly as it cools in the evening. The warm rising air currents stir up particles of dust and draw them aloft in a spinning column which we call dust devils.

Winds from the tropics tend to blow northward toward the end of the summer bringing rain and heat to Southern California. The people living there recognize these winds and refer to them as tropical storms. These same winds will blow on northward across the Gulf of California. When they reach the hot Arizona desert, the moist tropical air is heated even more and up it goes, thousands of feet into the sky. The lower pressures at the higher altitudes expand and cool the air, causing it to become saturated with condensing moisture until out it comes as a deluge of rain. There is so much water precipitated so rapidly that there is not enough time for it all to sink into the dry sand. Instead, much water runs off at a terrifying speed. Where it accumulates in dry washes that were eroded by previous floods, it makes a clean sweep, as it rushes along with a loud roar, carrying sand, mud, shrubs, and trees—anything that gets in its way. Such phenomena are known as flash floods because of the suddenness with which they come and go. They can be anticipated, especially in the summertime, when the tropical winds arrive from the south.

The strongest windstorms of the fall and winter in Southern California, known as santanas, reach very high velocities and follow a definite pressure pattern on the desert. First, a low-pressure area will move into the desert with the usual expanding of the air by decompression. This makes the air light and it rises high in the sky. Along comes a high-pressure area. This compresses the air and makes it more dense. Consequently, all the air that had gone up now comes down. The wind that results is called a compression wind. Not only has it been compressed by the barometric pressure that has risen in the area but it is also subject to greatly increased pressure of the low altitude to which it has descended. Thus it is doubly compressed and heated.

The air pumped into a bicycle tire will get hot, due to the compression caused by the piston of the pump. The piston of a diesel engine compresses the fuel, heating it so much that it ignites. Just so, the santanas are very hot desert winds heated by compression. They will usually blow consecutively for not more than a day and a night. Since they blow from the land to the sea, they almost flatten the waves of the Southern California seacoast, but along the exposed easterly shores of the channel islands, some twenty-five miles at sea the waves become mountainous. Through the years, scores of boats have been swept onto the beach and destroyed in the harbor of Avalon, Santa Catalina Island, which is a good shelter for all of the Southern California storms except the santana from the desert. Besides the santanas of California deserts, there are two other famous compression winds, the chinook of the Rocky Mountains and the foehn of the Alps.

It has already been explained that the descending air in the horse latitudes is heated by compression and how this air, as it blows across the land toward the equator, is heated even more. These winds are known as trade winds. They are not strictly compression winds because there is a lot more than compression involved in their existence. Compression winds are local and seasonal and the trade winds are not seasonal and they travel thousands of miles from a place of high pressure at the horse latitudes to a place of low pressure at the equator. The rotation of the earth has an additional effect on the way they blow in a clockwise direction in the Northern Hemisphere and counterclockwise in the Southern Hemisphere. Such a trade wind is

The accordion pleats of the saguaro cactus of the Arizona Desert make possible considerable expansion of the stem when the plant takes up the water of a summer cloudburst.

Crescent shaped barchanes, such as this one at Death Valley, are traveling dunes.

the harmattan of Africa, which blows across the Sahara. It is constantly dry and dusty and becomes even more so as it approaches the hotter equator. The deserts of southwestern United States are not directly affected by trade winds because they lie north of the horse latitudes, but the trade winds have a very definite drying effect on the deserts of Mexico.

The sirocco is a hot, dusty wind that blows from the Sahara over the Mediterranean, in the vicinity of Algeria, and the khamsin is a wind that may blow ceaselessly for two days in Egypt and do serious damage to vegetation.

DESERT SOIL

The scarcity of water on the desert accounts for the lack of abundant plant and animal life, both of which are necessary for the production of fertile soil. The plants must first free the minerals of the rocks by chemical action, the most important of which is the production of the acid-forming carbon dioxide, which dissolves the rocks. Once the plants have secured a foothold, their roots grow larger and split the rocks mechanically. Dead plants and animals decay and produce minerals that are essential for further plant growth, which results in more and more breakdown of rocks and the production of fertile soil. This fertile soil is fine and light compared to rock, gravel, and sand, and unless there are lots of plant roots to hold it in place, the

22

wind will blow it away and the infrequent rains will wash it out, leaving rock, gravel, and sand behind. Sometimes the desert winds blow hard enough to waft the sand away, leaving bare rock, which is known as desert pavement.

Any mixture of rock, gravel, sand, and fertile soil will in time end up in layers, with the larger particles on top and the finer particles at the bottom. The sand and soil would tend to filter down under the rocks and gravel. Shake these materials in a box and the rocks will end up on top. But this doesn't happen in regions where there are plant roots to hold the fertile soil at the surface.

SAND DUNES

Most of the deserts of the world have places that are nearly all sand. Sand comes from crumbled rocks and is the result of erosion by extreme temperatures that expand and contract the rock. Also, moisture in cracks of rocks becomes ice, expands and breaks off pieces of them. Some of the sand is washed down from rocks on nearby mountains.

In the southwestern United States, the famous White Sands of New Mexico are composed of grains of gypsum. This contains calcium sulfate from which plaster is made. Gypsum rocks are not common on the surface. The most abundant exposed rocks are granite, which contain quartz (silicon dioxide) and feldspar. The latter mineral combines potassium and aluminum plus silicon. Quartz is one of the most durable materials that exists. Indian arrowheads were made of quartz because it is so difficult to chip. Feldspar breaks easily in what are known as cleavage plains. After granite has been eroded, about all that is left is quartz, which explains why desert sand, and beach sand, too, is practically nothing but quartz particles.

As we have seen, the temperature of sand rises quickly with a little sunshine. This causes any moisture that is present to evaporate quickly. Without anything to hold the grains of sand together, they are easily picked up by the strong desert winds and carried for miles. Desert sandstorms cause much damage to automobile windshields because the sand is harder than the glass and travels at high speeds.

Red Rock Canyon in the Mojave Desert of California. Joshua trees are in the foreground. The rocks are red due to the iron content. The layers are distinct because layers of lake sediment are alternately covered with lava from volcanoes that erupted about twenty thousand years ago. There is located here a sedimentary rock formation known as the Ricardo. Fossils of horses, camels and antelope have been found in the formation and are thought to be about ten million years old.

When winds carrying sand meet obstructions such as creosote bushes or other desert plants, eddy currents are formed in back of the plants and the wind is slowed down. The sand is dropped. In time, huge piles of sand accumulate in such places. They are called sand dunes. The sandstorms that produce them are quite often terrifying, but the dunes that are formed are beautiful.

Whereas dunes cover the northern third of the Sahara Desert, they are not numerous in the southwestern United States, where they cover about 2 per cent of the desert area. The best known are near Stovepipe Wells, in Death Valley. Some of the most extensive dunes —and possibly the oldest—are on the southwestern shores of the Salton Sea, in the Coachella Valley, south of Palm Springs, California. There are some traveling dunes here which are characteristically crescent shaped. They are called barchans. The barchans of Libya travel fifty feet a year and cover almost anything that lies in their path.

3

History of the Desert

Bare rocks make the desert a paradise for geologists, who read the history of the earth from the record written in the rocks, and for paleontologists, who study fossils and learn about the plants and animals that used to live here. The two sciences are naturally closely related. Since certain species had limited life spans, they serve as key fossils to identify the strata in which they were discovered. Also, fossils of marine animals identify certain sedimentary rocks as once having been the floor of the ocean.

The history of the region becomes increasingly obscure as the scientists go back in time, but the past half billion years present a clear picture, largely because of the abundance of fossils that have been located and identified. In fact, this five-hundred-million-year span has been divided into three eras on the basis of the key fossils that identify the rocks of each era. Paleozoic in Greek means ancient (*paleo*) life (*zoic*). The Paleozoic Era started five hundred million years ago and ended three hundred million years later. During all this time, the ocean covered most of the western United States. At first there were only marine invertebrates—protozoa, sponges, corals, brachiopods, worms, ancient mollusks such as snails and clams, ancestors of modern starfish and sea urchins. The most abundant of all were the trilobites, those joint-legged relatives of the horseshoe crab of the Atlantic seacoast. Since the trilobites were relatively short-lived, they are the key fossils that identify this ancient rock strata. They are found in exposed Paleozoic rock in the White and Inyo mountains, on the westernmost edge of the Mojave Desert, near Death Valley, in California.

The oldest vertebrate fossils are fish. These are found in rock of the Paleozoic Era that dates back three hundred million years. So far, there is no record of such fossils having been taken from the rocks of the deserts of the Southwest, but they are present in a layer of limestone and sandstone about a quarter of a mile above the Colorado River, in the Grand Canyon, in Arizona, on the far east boundary of the Mojave Desert. About a thousand feet below the south rim of the Grand Canyon, on the Hermit Trail, there is a layer of sandstone formed from a sand dune that existed a little more than two hundred million years ago. In this there are fossils of primitive amphibians and reptiles, the first vertebrates to make an attempt to leave the sea and adapt themselves to a life on land. In a layer of shale, which once was mud, perhaps from a swamp, are found fossils of some of the first land plants, giant tree ferns which may have grown to a height of forty feet. The most primitive plants were algae or seaweeds, fossils of which are found with the trilobites in the White and Inyo mountains.

The second division of the span of time is known as the Mesozoic Era, which means in Greek middle life era. It extended from two hundred million to sixty million years ago and is known as the age of reptiles. During this era there were depressions of the continent, with the invasion of the sea that covered the western part of the United States, but there was also an elevation of the land and here the sea receded to leave a vast coastal plain.

Over the middle third of the era there was a warm, moist climate, an ideal environment for reptiles. Swamps and forests of tree ferns dotted the western United States. At that time, one group of reptiles known as dinosaurs reached their peak of development. In Greek dinosaur means terrible lizard. Brontosaurus was a dinosaur that grew to be as long as eighty feet and weighed nearly forty tons. Some of these creatures were so big they couldn't support their own weight, so they lived in swamps to get support from the buoyancy of water. The fern forests were their food. In northwestern Colorado, the Green River has cut down into the Mesozoic rock there to expose the fossils of dinosaurs. Footprints of dinosaurs have been found in Mesozoic rock in the Mojave Desert of southern Nevada. It is difficult for us to visualize swamps and ferns in what is now a very dry desert.

Over this same period of time, the Sierra Nevada and Rocky Mountains began to rise until, toward the end of the Mesozoic Era, about a hundred million years ago, a rain shadow became so extensive that the swamps dried up and the ferns died off—and with them the dinosaurs. In addition, one of the most extensive inundations by the sea took place, from the Gulf of Mexico across the plains as far east as the Rockies and northward nearly to the Arctic.

The Cenozoic Era, meaning era of recent life in Greek, began sixty million years ago and includes the present time. This is the age of birds and mammals, whose fossils identify the rocks of the era in the Mojave Desert of California. There are fossils of three-toed horses about the size of small colts, and of both small camels and some specimens as large as modern camels, as well as of a four-tusked mastodon related to elephants, large and small antelopes, wild pigs, large and small cats, wolflike dogs, and saber-toothed cats the size of present-day lions. The most ancient of these fossils are twenty million years old. They are found at Barstow, California. Others, ten million years old, are found near the town of Ricardo. The most recent were discovered in Manix Lake bed along the road to Las Vegas. They are probably quite recent, resembling very closely the fossils taken from the La Brea Tar Pits, in Los Angeles, that date back just fourteen thousand years.

Duckbill dinosaur fossil bones found in California are on display in the Los Angeles County Museum. The duck-like bill had the same function as the bill of the duck, to strain food out of the water.

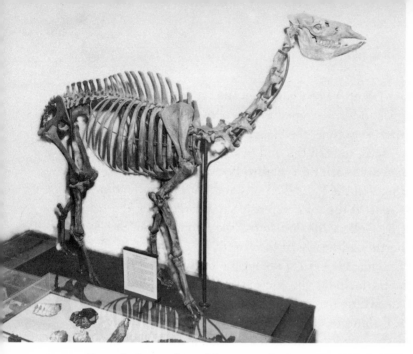

Yesterday's camel fossil bones on display at the Los Angeles County Museum.

Horses, camels, mastodons, and antelopes are strictly grazing animals. There must have been, therefore, grassland to feed them, with plenty of rain to make the grass grow. Snail shells resembling existing fresh-water species give evidence that there were lakes. The conclusion is that the present deserts of the southwest United States are quite young, geologically speaking. The mountains that were built in the Mesozoic Era were eroded away during the first part of the Cenozoic, permitting sea breezes to bring rain. During the last twenty million years, these mountains have been rebuilding. The present elevation was reached a million years ago, and the southwestern United States became a desert.

During the Cenozoic Era, there were many more animals living on the great fertile coastal plane of southwestern United States than were living in the deserts as the scarcity of fossil finds would indicate. According to the fossil record so well preserved in the tar pits at Rancho La Brea, on Wilshire Boulevard in Los Angeles, fourteen thousand years ago, toward the end of the last of four ice ages that stated a million years ago, horses, camels, mastodons, antelopes, wild pigs, large and small cats, wolflike dogs, huge ground sloths, and saber-toothed cats crowd themselves out to the seacoast of Southern California, in hopes of finding food. Those that didn't starve to death or become the meal of a saber-toothed cat were trapped in the tar and died a tragic death. Their bones are so well preserved and have been so skillfully reconstructed that the exhibit at the Los Angeles County Museum gives a remarkably clear picture of how these animals looked and, knowing their food requirements, what the climate and vegetation were like. Why did most of them become extinct? Probably because of the mountains that turned their pastureland into a dry desert and the ice ages that brought cold and further depletion of their food supply.

The last place where one would expect to find camels and llamas living in the wild is North America, but it was there that they came into being during the Cenozoic Era. During the ice ages, there was so much ocean water on land in the form of ice that the sea level was lowered about six hundred feet. This was enough to expose submerged land and form land bridges between the continents of North and South America and between North America and Asia, where the Bering Strait is located. Some of the llamas escaped to South America, where there was a more suitable climate and food supply. The camels crossed over to Asia, as did the horses, many of them ending up in the Gobi Desert. During the dry years, the camels adapted themselves to a successful desert life by storing food in the hump and water in the tissues all over the body. Under average desert conditions, a camel can go without drinking water for as long as two weeks. The horse adapted itself by developing great speed in traveling across the desert sand from one water hole and food supply to another.

ANTHROPOLOGY OF THE DESERT

The first humans to come to North America were probably Mongolians from Asia who had become used to a life in the Gobi Desert, so they seemed to be at home in the deserts of North America. In effect, the Mongolians had traded places with the camels, who settled immediately in the Gobi Desert and later moved on to the

Sahara and Arabian deserts. We are told by anthropologists that the Mongolians became the North American Indians. They arrived here about twenty thousand years ago. When the Spaniards landed in Mexico in the sixteenth century, they brought horses with them. The horse that had left by way of the land bridge came back in a Spanish galleon. The Indians captured the strays. By the time the first wagon trains arrived in the desert, toward the beginning of the nineteenth century, the Indians were such good horseback riders and marksmen with their bows and arrows that they were a formidable foe for the pioneers, who called the Cheyennes, Comanches, and Kiowas "the devils of the desert."

The first white pioneers to cross the desert found such a hostile land that everything possible was done to avoid it. For many, it was preferable to spend at least four months sailing around Cape Horn, at the southern tip of South America, a place described as the point of origin of the most fearful storms at sea, than to risk the perils of starvation, thirst, and attacks by Indians on the desert. Others chose to take the risk of death by yellow fever and travel west by way of the Isthmus of Panama.

But there were many who did brave the desert wastes and, as Horace Greeley wrote in 1859, "along the whole route across the desert are the remains of men, animals and wrecks of camps and wagons that tell the story of suffering, robbery, outrage."

The Mormons left Illinois for the Great Basin Desert in 1847 and established Salt Lake City. When gold was discovered in California in 1849, this city became a sort of jumping-off place, the last point of habitation, where the wagon trains fitted out before starting across the desert. In 1848, a party known as the Jayhawkers from Illinois, while reorganizing in Salt Lake City, decided to avoid the perils of the Overland Trail to Reno and the Sierra, where the Donner party had died in the twenty-foot snows, and go south along the Mormon trail, through the Mojave Desert by way of Vegas Springs, to San Bernardino in California and thence northward to the gold fields in the Sierra. About halfway to Las Vegas, the party decided that the Mormon trail was too slow and they took a disastrous short cut to

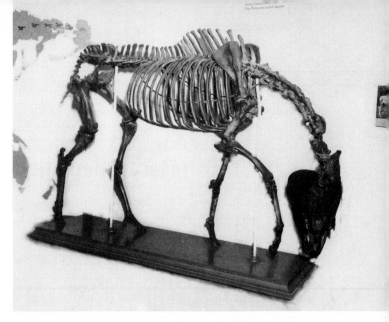

Fossil bones of the western horse of California are 50,000 years old. They are on display in the Los Angeles County Museum. Upper left hand corner of display shows horses migrating from North America to Asia as did the camels during the ice ages.

the Sierra, which would have brought them to the foot of Mount Whitney—perhaps without incident—had not the most treacherous of deserts and the lowest place in the Western Hemisphere, 282 feet below sea level, stood in their way. Before they reached the Sierra, many of them died from thirst and starvation. This tragic place, that is now a national monument, was named Death Valley. Today, an air-conditioned resort hotel and other modern accommodations welcome many vacationers to this fascinating area.

The moisture-free skies of a desert make the vision far and the distances dangerously deceptive. The pioneers in their covered wagons knew little about the desert. What appeared to them to be a few hours' trip across the hot, burning sands of the Mojave to their goal, a mountain stream of melted snow water, fresh from the fourteen-thousand-foot crest of the Sierra, turned out to be hundreds of miles away. Had they known this, they would have conserved what water they had and tried other precautionary ways, such as traveling at night in the absence of the blazing sun—or maybe they would not have started at all.

4

Plant Adaptations

LICHENS

Lichens are plants that grow on bare rocks. They are very abundant on the rocks of the desert and come in many colors, especially reds, yellows, and greens. Everyone notices lichens without realizing what unusual plants they are. They are a combination of algae intertwined in the tissues of fungi. In order to live, each plant must have the other. Algae have chlorophyll, the enzyme essential for food manufacture by photosynthesis. The fungi have no chlorophyll, so they are always dependent upon other organisms to supply their nutrient requirements, being parasitic on live plants and animals or saprophytic on dead organisms. In the case of lichens, the fungi and the algae have a relationship of mutual benefit known as symbiotic. The fungi receive their food from the algae, but, in return, the algae receive from the fungi the minerals necessary for photosynthesis that only the fungi are capable of extracting from the rock. Seemingly, because neither organism could survive without the other, the spores that reproduce the fungi and those that reproduce the algae will germinate only if each is in contact with the other. How carefully the problems of survival for living things have been solved!

Land plants are dependent upon lichens to prepare the minerals of rocks so that they will be available to them. Lichens are able to grow on bare rocks and convert sufficient quantities of the minerals of those rocks into minerals that are usable for making their own food. As the lichens die, bacteria convert the food stored in their tissues into minerals which the other plants can use in their own photosynthesis or manufacture of food.

The order in which other plants follow the lichens in places where there is plenty of water, such as an oasis, is as follows: first moss

Lichens are very successful bare rock dwellers.

plants, then ferns, and finally seed plants, with the simpler plants preparing the way for the more complex. This progression is known to biologists as plant succession. In the hot, dry places of the desert, mosses and ferns are unable to grow, so plant succession does not occur in its entirety. This partially explains why the seed plants have such difficulty in getting started.

TREES AND SHRUBS

Palm trees will grow only where there is a plentiful supply of water. Just as the date palms of the Arabian and Saharan deserts grow where there is spring water in an oasis, so do the California fan palms take root in the Colorado Desert of Southern California. They

California fan palms, also known as Washingtonia fan palms in honor of the first president, photographed at Palm Canyon at the foot of Mt. San Jacinto, Palm Springs, California.

Spiny mesquite makes a wonderful briar patch for rabbits to take shelter. Also they eat the bark. The blossoms will soon ripen into pods filled with nutritious beans.

do not always lead the way to good drinking water, however, because they are very tolerant of an alkaline content, which makes water unfit for human consumption.

These native California palms have been transplanted to gardens all over the world where it is warm enough for them to grow. In Hawaii and Algeria, they are so abundant they appear to be native trees. In Hawaii, they are called hula palms because the dead fronds that remain attached to the trunks of the trees hang down like grass skirts. Most of the desert plants have learned by adaptation to go without water for long periods of time, but anyone who has kept a potted palm tree in the house knows that it must be watered often.

The largest natural grove of California fan palms is in Palm Canyon, at Palm Springs, California, at the foot of towering Mount San Jacinto. There is plenty of spring water here because the great quantities of water collected as rain and snow on the mountain give a high water table.

Directly east of Palm Springs, a few miles across the sand dunes, palm trees grow along the San Andreas fault, one of the most active earthquake faults in the Southwest. It is closely associated with

Mesquite beans and pods were gathered in baskets by the Cahilla Indians who live to this day in the Colorado Desert of Southern California.

mountain building there. The palm trees help to locate the fault because its action causes a damming up of ground water, bringing it nearer to the surface and causing it to accumulate in sufficient quantities to meet the water requirements of these trees.

Mesquite, pronounced by Texans and most other people "mez keet," is another tree of high-water requirements. It has tender green leaves which look out of place on a hot, dry desert. It has, however, its own special way of solving the surface water-shortage problem. It sends roots far down into the soil for water. One investigator dug out a root that was one hundred and eighty feet long and the diameter of the root at this point was still at least half as much as it was at the start of the root, indicating that there were many more feet of the root down in the ground. This adaptation makes the mesquite one of the most successful of desert plants. It grows best in the alluvial soil of flood plains and dry lake basins. Because it will grow only where there is ground water, it makes a good indicator for a place to dig a well.

The mistletoe that grows on mesquite has red berries that are relished by the phainopepla.

Phainopeplas are fly-catchers that are also fond of berries.

Since a mesquite seedling has high-water requirements, in an area where the ground water is thirty to a hundred feet below the surface of the soil, its roots would have to be that same length. The mystery is how does the seedling get started and what does it do for water before the roots reach the underground water? Some scientists say that it might be the "once in a hundred years or so" wet summers and winters that get the mesquite seedlings started.

Mesquite wood, and especially the underground stems, makes fine firewood for desert campers. Mesquite trees have always been the most important desert plants for the Indian tribes of the Southwest. The pillars to support their houses, the horizontal stringers of the roof and the siding were often built with mesquite stems.

Mesquite is a member of the pea family and has pods filled with beans. Not only are the beans highly nutritious, but, so are the pods. The Indians ate them either raw or boiled. The long, straight pod has a high sugar content and tastes sweet, which has given the plant the name, honey mesquite. The Indians ground the beans into flour for cakes and mush. Had the Jayhawkers, of Death Valley known the value of mesquite pods and beans, they need not have suffered from starvation.

Not only do the pods and beans of mesquite serve as food for most desert mammals as well as domestic cattle, but there is a species of mistletoe that is parasitic on mesquite. It has large berries which are a favorite food for some birds, especially the phainopepla. The feathers of this bird are a striking, shiny black. It has a crest on its head and a brilliant red eye that gives it the Greek name, phaino-pepla.

The phainopepla depends upon these mistletoe berries for a major portion of its diet. It insures an adequate supply by planting its own mistletoe. It eats the berries and digests the fruit. The seeds pass through its body undigested and drop on the mesquite branches. The seeds produce a gummy material that not only prevents the digestive juices of the bird from acting on them but also causes them to adhere firmly to the mesquite branches. As the embryo root grows and touches the stem, the mesquite responds by exuding a clear, translucent resin which pushes the seed and its root away. The valiant mesquite thus prevents itself from being overrun by the mistletoe, for nearly always, the seed will use up its energy in the struggle to reach the mesquite stem and will finally die off. Only the hardiest of the seeds successfully implant their roots in the stem of the mesquite and thus insure a future supply of berries for the nourishment of the phainopepla.

The creosote bush of the desert covers its leaves with wax and in this way prevents excessive evaporation and loss of water. It gets its name from the odor of its waxy leaves. These are olive green when moisture is sufficient, but when drought comes, the color changes to brownish green, as the leaves shrivel to reduce the evaporation surface. If the drought continues, the leaves drop off.

The mesquite produces a resin-like sap to protect itself from sprouting mistletoe seeds by pushing the seed away so that the root can't reach the mes-quite.

Creosote bush roots reach out widely to extract moisture from the soil. The bushes are usually far apart and evenly spaced in areas of the desert where the land is dry. In this way, excessive competition for small quantities of moisture is avoided. Some scientists are working on a hypothesis that the bushes produce a chemical that prevents seeds of their own and other plants from germinating near them. Other scientists claim that such a chemical has not been conclusively demonstrated and that the reason why other seeds do not germinate near by is that the first plant to grow in the area takes most of the moisture. Along paved desert roads, where moisture tends to accumulate and run off the edges, creosote bushes are not spaced. In fact, they grow in such numbers they tend to crowd one another.

Creosote bushes are so strictly a plant of the true southwest desert of North America that they are not successfully transplanted. One of the best of all plant indicators of the desert is the creosote bush.

Creosote bushes are the most widespread of strictly desert plants. In the background is an agave which is also known as a century plant. It has bayonet-like sharp pointed basal leaves and a stalk that bears flowers.

Smoke trees grow in the Colorado Desert dry washes where they take advantage of the few and far between flash floods to supply their minimum water requirements.

Smoke trees grow almost exclusively in the dry washes of the Colorado Desert of Southern California. From a distance, they resemble a wisp of gray smoke, which gives them their name. In the early summer they come into bloom, with small blossoms of brilliant blue.

The smoke trees have extremely tough seed coats, except when they are very fresh, and only a strong force will crack them open so that they can germinate. The desert being dry, fresh seeds do not usually receive enough moisture to germinate, which explains why the smoke trees grow in the dry washes, where the flash floods are quite often violent. The seeds will be tumbled and ground by the turbulent water until they crack open. One investigator has observed that smoke tree seedlings spring up one hundred and fifty to three hundred feet downstream from the parent tree. The explanation is that, if the seeds are dragged by the flood over three hundred feet, they will be pulverized and destroyed but, in order to be cracked open sufficiently for germination, they must be ground for at least one hundred and fifty feet. The next time you see smoke trees, make note whether your observations support this theory.

The paloverde tree has brilliant green, chlorophyll filled stems, and beautiful yellow flowers in the late spring.

In Spanish, paloverde means green tree. The trunk and branches of the paloverde have great quantities of chlorophyll to carry on the photosynthesis needs of the plant, because most of the year the tree is without leaves which otherwise would do the job. It loses its leaves shortly after they are sprouted, which prevents much loss of water by transpiration. As we have seen illustrated many times it isn't so much that desert plants do not need water but they have learned to conserve what water they get. The paloverde is related to the smoke tree, being a member of the pea family. It has brilliant yellow blossoms late in the spring which in combination with the green branches makes a striking color effect.

Like the smoke tree, the paloverde depends upon flash floods in dry washes to supply its water requirements. It, too, has a seed with a tough coat that seems to need the abrasive action of the flood to break open the coat and permit the tree to grow.

Joshua trees identify the Mojave Desert, just as smoke trees are indicators of the Colorado Desert. They are actually yuccas and members of the lily family. Their leaves are parallel veined, like the leaves of bulbs. They are also narrow and thick-skinned to slow down evaporation. The Joshua trees become giants forty feet high. They were named by the Mormons, who traveled through the heart of the Mojave Desert, in the State of Nevada, on their way from Salt Lake City to San Bernardino. The scraggly, grotesque branching of the limbs of the Joshua tree were said by the Mormons to resemble the arms of Joshua, beckoning to them to come west. At least this idea gave them courage as they traveled westward through the inhospitable desert. The large white blossoms are lily-like and the seeds that follow are quite large and nutritious and a favorite food of the antelope ground squirrels that are found in large numbers where the Joshua trees grow. See photograph below.

Joshua trees characterize the Mojave Desert as the smoke trees do the Colorado Desert of Southern California.

Ocotillo is a shrub that grows abundantly in the desert areas of southwestern United States and Mexico. It has underground stems, with only the branches exposed above the ground. This is part of its method for conserving moisture. The leaves are scalelike and reduced in size, which decreases the evaporation. The branches are so covered with resin for the retention of water that they burn brightly and are used by the Indians for candles and torches. In the sixteenth century, the Aztecs called ocotillo candlewood. The flowers, which are located in dense clusters along the tips of the branches, are flame red. Automobile and train passengers can enjoy the beautiful ocotillo starting in southern Texas and moving all the way across southern New Mexico and Arizona to the Colorado Desert of Southern California.

Cactus plants are native to the North American continent and certain neighboring islands, but they have been transplanted all over the world. They are not strictly an indicator of the desert, but they are indicators of arid and semi-arid regions, such as the coastal plane

Antelope ground squirrels are easily identified by the short white tails they carry over their backs so that they resemble a pronghorned antelope in flight.

The Gila woodpecker digs a nest in the stem of a saguaro. The tail of a woodpecker comes in handy as a prop to help support itself in its precarious perch.

of Southern California and the Channel Islands offshore. Nevertheless, they are more abundant on the desert than elsewhere. They have very shallow root systems, which quickly gather up the little surface water that accumulates infrequently. Also, the leaves of cactus plants have been reduced to spines to decrease the evaporation surface. The stems of these plants are specialists in storing water. They are pulpy and sometimes, as in the case of the famous desert barrel cactus, wringing wet. The water in the latter is practically tasteless and there is plenty to save the lives of thirsty desert travelers who are fortunate enough to find a barrel cactus.

Saguaros are cactuses that are found mostly in the Colorado Desert of western Arizona because it is here that summer cloudbursts are quite regular and frequent. The saguaro is about the thickest and tallest of any of the desert plants, reaching a height of thirty or forty feet. The stems are pleated like an accordion, to permit expansion and contraction. As much as a ton of water may be taken into the saguaro's stems during one deluge from a summer cloudburst, which has already been described as a result of warm, moist, tropical winds

The elf owl's circular pupils dilate and constrict with the slightest light changes. Extreme dilation at night aids the night vision of this nocturnal animal.

moving northward across the Gulf of California. During the dry months that follow, the plant uses so much of its stored water that the stems shrink, forming deep wrinkles or pleats.

Most saguaros are riddled with holes, dug by the Gila woodpeckers for nests. The following year, when these nests are deserted by their original tenants, the smallest owl in the world, the five-inch-high elf owl of the southwest desert, quite often moves in.

ANNUALS

Annuals are plants that come and go each year as distinguished from the shrubs, trees and flowers that may live on and on and are called perennials. The southwest desert has around seven hundred species of annuals that are especially adapted to the environment which is unlike that of any other region of the world. The seeds are scattered by the wind and then lie dormant—for years, if necessary—waiting for rain. Not just any amount of rain will do. Scientists have evidence that the seeds are surrounded with a water-soluble chemical that must be washed away before they will even start to sprout.

44

This is called a germination inhibitor. In the laboratory, it has been determined that it takes at least an inch of rainfall to wash out the inhibitor. In exactly what way the dormant perennial seed can tell just how much rain has fallen, was a mystery, since a tenth of an inch of precipitation will make the upper inch of soil, where the seeds lie, just as wet as two inches of rain. Investigation has shown that the wetness of the soil doesn't count but rather how much rain sprinkles on top of the seeds and washes the inhibitors down into the soil. As a result, the plant is assured that there is going to be enough moisture to see it through its life span before the seeds are permitted to sprout. If it were not for this carefully devised mechanism, the sprouting would start prematurely and maybe there would not be enough moisture to keep it from withering before it had a chance to blossom and make seeds—and so reproduce itself before it dies.

The details are even further planned. Once the requirements for germination have been met, the plant anticipates the dry conditions that will follow. By some miraculous adaptation, the desert annuals come into bloom faster than any other plants on earth. They form their seeds quickly and wither and die. Botanists call them ephemeral annuals, which means they are short-lived. Most years, flowers are scarce on the desert, but, with a little rain, almost every foot of sandy and gravelly soil comes into bloom, to delight the desert traveler.

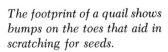

The footprint of a quail shows bumps on the toes that aid in scratching for seeds.

5

Animal Adaptations

Most desert animals go under cover in the daytime. For this reason, people think that there are no animals on the desert. The numerous tracks left by animals on the desert sand show that this is not so. Each animal has its own signature. Where there is more sand than rock, especially around sand dunes, these signatures are distinctly written and by their freshness an observer can tell just how recently the animal passed that way.

Quail find seeds in the desert sand. Like their relatives, the chickens, they scratch for their food. They have a foot that was designed so that it can do the very best job of scratching. What could be better for scratching than a rake? Scratching birds have a rake-like foot. All along the underside of the bones of the foot are bony projections, very much like the tines of a rake. The footprint of a quail shows at least four or five little bumps or tines on the toes. If the tracks lead from under a bush on the opposite side from which the desert explorer is walking, chances are the quail ran under the bush to hide when it heard approaching footsteps.

The Le Conte thrasher is a desert bird that can be identified by its ashy-gray color and its long bill that curves down. Also it is a beautiful singer. It sounds a little like a mockingbird. The thrasher's bill is well designed for reaching insects that scurry along the sand and for probing under the sand for those insects that have buried themselves to escape. The foot of this bird is useful in running across the sand which the bird does lots of with great long strides. The strides help to identify the footprints of Le Conte thrasher. An experienced desert sleuth may find the tracks of a desert sand beetle suddenly terminating where they meet the striding footprints of the thrasher.

46

Sand beetles and other insects have three pairs of feet and as they walk along three pairs of dots are imprinted over and over again. Spiders and their relatives the scorpions have four pairs which leave an undeterminable number of dots but in a regular pattern. The tarantula, a large desert spider, has such a bulky body that it tends to drag in the sand, leaving its mark between the footprints. The tarantula spider has a bad reputation because it has big jaws for eating grasshoppers and beetles and for protection from its enemies including humans. The bite will cause very little irritation and it will never bite unless roughly treated. Its worst enemy is a wasp with a blue body and red wings, called a tarantula hawk. The wasp stings a tarantula causing paralysis but not death. It then drags the tarantula to its home in a hole in the ground where the young wasps have a fresh food supply for about two weeks. The long tail of the scorpion, that bares the stinger, drops periodically into the sand, leaving an

The centipede (left) and the scorpion are two venomous dwellers of the desert. These models are on display at the Palm Springs Desert Museum. The centipede has poison glands at the base of the jaw that open at the sharp tips of the poison claws, the first pair of appendages that resemble walking legs. The poison is used to subdue its prey, mostly insects, and for defense. Some can inject enough venom to be dangerous to a child or unhealthy adult. The scorpion eats soft bodied insects. This species of scorpion that lives west of the Colorado River may cause a painful sting and local swelling but it is not usually fatal to humans.

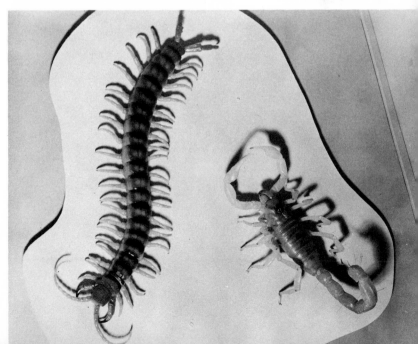

Bob cat, raised in captivity, is still wild and fierce and not at all tame. Bob cats are fast and have sharp claws for offense and defense.

oval-shaped mark which makes it easy to identify the treacherous animal. The large species that lives on the west side of the Colorado River gives a painful sting that probably is not fatal to man, but the smaller scorpions that live in the desert to the east give a more serious sting that has caused some deaths of humans. The usual use of the stinger is to kill its prey which is usually spiders, beetles, and moths. They catch and hold these with their two clawlike pincers and then bring the tail with its stinger up and over to sting the prey to death.

Coyote tracks resemble quite closely those of a large German shepherd dog. The most centrally located toe of each paw is longer than in the case of most dogs. Also, coyotes are said to mate for life and are unusually good family animals. Both father and mother take care of the pups. They go hunting together just before dawn which makes this the best time to see them. Almost always when there are coyote tracks there are the footprints of two animals, sometimes one following the other and then walking side by side.

Kit fox tracks are also quite doglike but less than a quarter the size of the average adult coyote tracks. Since the favorite food of a kit fox is a kangaroo rat that lives in a burrow in the sand, kit fox tracks are often found in areas where the kangaroo rats are abundant. The footprints of the kangaroo rat are squirrel-like in size and shape, but unlike squirrels the kangaroo rat continuously uses its very long

48

Road runners are among the most striking personalities of the cactus covered desert, where they build their nests preferably in cholla.

tail to keep its balance as it waltzes and runs. When it is not moving, the tail will leave an imprint between the footprints in the sand.

Road runners cover much territory as they run across the desert sands looking for lizards and snakes for food. They seldom fly for more than the distance of a short jump. Their tracks are some of the most abundant and certainly the most easily identified because they are so different from those of any other desert birds. Being members of the cuckoo family, two toes of each foot are directed forward and the other two toes backward. All of the other bird tracks on the desert sand will be three toes forward and one backward on each foot.

The last place on the desert in which we would expect to find animal life is a sand dune. Life in shifting, wind-blown sand seems impossible. Yet living things are here in numbers. The rippled sand

Road runner tracks are very numerous on the sandy desert. They are the only bird tracks that have two toe marks forward and two toe marks backward.

at close range shows the traces of beetles, scorpions, wingless, burrowing roaches, and a host of other humble animals.

Whereas animals living elsewhere on the desert have a choice of things to give them shelter, as rocks and crevices for the chuckwalla, palm fronds for the nesting places of the canyon wrens and orioles, the protection of thorny cholla cactus for the cactus wren and roadrunner nests, for the animals of the dunes, the only place to go and hide is in the sand.

If at first the dunes seem empty, look for tracks. Tracks remain from storm to storm or at least until erased by sand movement. But the animal that makes them is gone in seconds. Follow the tracks and quite often the animal can be found, sheltered in a burrow in the sand.

The basic food substance of all animals is plant life because only plants by photosynthesis can manufacture food for animals. Some animals are strictly plant eaters. Others do not eat plants but they eat animals that do. In the sand dunes the beetles and roaches are the plant eaters. They are said to be vegetarians. As we learned in the chapter on plants, the seeds of the ephemeral annuals are scattered plentifully over the sand. Once the seeds sprout, the insects

Walking-sticks are insects that live where there are twigs and stems upon which they feed. Of all the camouflages of nature none is more effective.

The kangaroo rat runs by jumping like a kangaroo, using only the hind legs. This photo was taken at 1/5000 of a second to partially stop the action.

grow and multiply, feeding on the tender, succulent vegetation while it is available, then scurrying under ground to lay a batch of long-lived eggs or eggs that hatch and form pupae or cocoons that last a long time and await the next and often distant rains. Late in the season the dead plant stalks supply some food to limited numbers of hardy insects, such as the harvester ants.

In the sand dunes wherever there is a strong-rooted bush to give some support to the sand, there will almost always be found the burrows of kangaroo rats. The sand is easy to dig in and will be

A kangaroo rat is really a squirrel. It doesn't drink water under any circumstances as far as is known today.

Ocellated sand lizards have markings on their backs that give them the appearance of the sand in which they live. Their noses are blunt and shovel shaped for digging in.

riddled with tunnels. These squirrel-like animals have long kangaroo-like rear legs and they can jump along as fast as thirty miles per hour. Their front legs are short and have paws which are used almost exclusively for stuffing seeds into their whiskered faces. Their diet is almost entirely seeds. As far as is known they do not drink water. They are known as the rat that never drinks. Scientific experiments show that they meet most of their water requirements by oxidizing food containing hydrogen. In other words, oxygen plus hydrogen gives water. However, when animals breathe in oxygen they also lose much water from the lungs by evaporation so it is impossible to meet water requirements by this process alone. The kangaroo rat comes closest to it of any known animal, but even the kangaroo rat needs a little help which it apparently gets from moisture that is taken up by the seeds. Even in very dry desert areas there is apt to be humid air in the burrows where the animals live and store the seeds.

Besides the vegetarians, the sand dunes have their predators or meat eaters. As we have already learned the kangaroo rats are the main diet of the kit fox. As for the insects the scorpions take a large share. The scorpions are especially fond of the roaches, but they also eat beetles and moths.

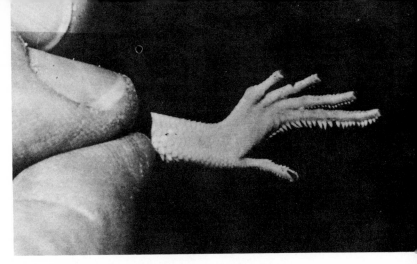

The sand lizard's toes are equipped with fringes of long pointed scales.

So are lizards fond of insects and especially beetles. Of all the lizards adapted to a desert life the most noteworthy is the one that lives in the sand dunes. This is the beautiful, velvet-smooth, fringe-footed, or ocellated sand lizard, possibly our most successful vertebrate resident of the dunes. Instead of the swim fins that are used by people to move more easily through water, the fringe-footed lizard has fringes on its toes to help it to "swim" itself to shelter underneath the loose sand. Also, the fringes help it to walk on the sand, just as snowshoes help humans to walk on the snow. These valve-like, freely movable fringes fold tightly along the toes when the foot is pulled forward underneath the sand, then expand as they are thrust backward against the sand.

The individual footprints of a sand lizard are broad because of the large area covered by the fringed toes.

Kangaroo rats may be caught in a trap by using seeds for bait.

If the lizard is lying on top of the sand, especially in the dotted shade of sparse vegetation, the coloration of its spots and speckles blends so perfectly that, at a distance, the animal is almost invisible. It is obvious that, if its top were as snow-white as its lower surface, the lizard would be very conspicuous. Because of the iron content of their sand particles, some dunes are colored pink. The sand lizards living in such dunes are a rosy tone, to match the background dunes.

The problem of sand in the eyes has been met in these desert-dwelling lizards with every device that can be imagined. The eyelids are scalloped along their edges so that when they close they fit together perfectly and tightly, and seem to interlock, like a jigsaw puzzle. Besides, there is an inner fold, resembling another eyelid, that is moist and slides across the eye itself. Nevertheless, some sand does pass by these almost perfect devices. But this has been provided for, too. Almost immediately a mucous capsule surrounds the invading sand, which is then transferred by a movement of the eye-lids to the corner of the eye and then flicked off by a scratching movement of the lizard's hind leg.

To keep sand out of its nostrils, this adaptable sand lizard is equipped with muscles to close them off, just like valves. All but the very finest sand is kept out during sandstorms and when the lizard is below the surface of the sand. Here again mucus surrounds what sand manages to pass the barrier, so that it can be expelled from the mouth with no harm to the animal.

Everything about the sand lizard is suited for life in a sand dune. The head is wedge-shaped and the body and legs are flattened so that the least effort is necessary to dive down into the sand and the least amount of sand is needed to cover and conceal the body. If the lizard's tail is still showing above the sand, it can wiggle and vibrate it until it, too, is buried and out of sight and out of mind of predators that eat the lizard.

The banded gecko is a lizard with a voice—it makes a chirping sound. It is an insect eater.

Although there is seldom a witness to the attack by a predator on a lizard, there are marks in the sand that record the tragic capture and death. Hawks and eagles, particularly, soar overhead and dive down on the feeding lizards. Road runners follow the rims of the dunes, where they are apt to find the lizards basking in the early-morning sun. At night, foxes and coyotes may occasionally smell out the hidden animals where they lie buried in the sand. A few may also be captured by snakes at night. But at least the sand lizards do not have much competition from other species of lizards.

When and where and how this lizard came to live in the realm of the dunes can only be guessed at. All we know today is that gradual change, the process of evolution, led to its present fitness to live in a specialized environment. Each adaptation is of such specific purpose that scientists agree that definite laws of nature govern the process whereby, of all the lizards in the world, only the sand lizard has acquired fringes on its toes to help it travel through the sand, and special eyelids and valves to keep the sand out of its eyes and

The Gila monster is the only poisonous lizard in the United States. It is native to the Arizona Desert.

Desert tortoises have good toes for digging burrows in sandy hills where they get protection from the heat of the day and hibernate from October until March. They eat plants, flowers and all.

nostrils. Moreover, the only lizard having large lungs and a loose skin that make it possible for the animal to puff up with air and wedge itself into rocky crevices so firmly that hawks and eagles have difficulty pulling it out is the desert chuckwalla. This species lives exclusively where there are huge rock formations.

Of all the western reptiles the little night-crawling sidewinder or horned rattlesnake is most widely known—and universally feared! The names are descriptive; the first, sidewinder, refers to the curious method of locomotion. It rolls along like a wheel. This will be described in detail later. While the adjective preceding the second name is derived from the protruding scales which form hornlike projections above the eyes. As for the fear, this is unwarranted, the result of much undeserved notoriety. Left to itself, this rattlesnake is shy, inoffensive, and reluctant to reveal its presence, either by

The horned toad is a lizard with sharp spines for protection. When excited, blood vessels of the eye may burst causing blood to squirt and dismay a predator. It feeds on insects, preferring ants.

trying to escape or by taking aggressive action. By day, it usually lies in the shade of a bush, but, during the hottest weather, it hides underground, in the burrow of some other animal. When the sidewinder is stepped on, or prodded and goaded into action, however, there is a sudden change, a transformation in demeanor and action. Far from being passive, the little snake may suddenly become aggressive and lash out at its tormentor, reaching a stroke length fully one-half that of its body. On the other hand, what is even more surprising to the uninitiated, it may explode into action and lope off in search of undisturbed surroundings, where it can once more coil up, work itself downward into the sand, and, flush with the surface and nearly invisible, wait there in security until nightfall.

This little snake is so surprising and so unusual that, even though far from impressive at a casual glance, it has become a part of the folklore of the southwestern United States. Even far beyond its actual territory, any of the small or young rattlers of the West are apt to be called sidewinders.

In North America, the true sidewinder is found only in desert regions of the southwestern United States, the closely adjacent areas in Mexico, and lower California. It is obvious that its peculiar powers of locomotion are used only where vegetation is so scanty and so widely spaced that its method of travel can be employed efficiently. This means, of course, that it is confined to desert areas, especially those with sandy soil or wind-piled soil, forming sand dunes.

Besides the Southwest of the United States, only in the Sahara and nearby spaces with scanty vegetation has this method of locomotion been developed—and the snakes in the two areas are not even related to each other. Their only bond is that imposed or fostered by a specialized environment.

Chuckwallas are strictly vegetarians. They eat flowers and prefer yellow ones.

Bailey's collared lizard has long sharp claws to capture smaller lizards. It chases after its prey by running on its hind legs like a dinosaur.

Compared to other snakes, sidewinders are fast. Slowness can be fatal to them, especially when there is any appreciable distance between vegetation and other cooling shelter. If distances are too great, the heat of the sun may overcome the snake before it can reach shade.

This great speed is also perfect for quick maneuvering and dodging, by reversal of direction. In addition, a good proportion of the body is kept off the superheated sand. The more of the snake that is kept away from the dangerously hot sand, the greater the margin of safety it will have in traveling from one place to another. The ground temperature of the desert during the daytime is often far above the fatal limit for the horned rattlesnake.

The sidewinder is the easiest snake to track because of its method of locomotion and its habitat. It leaves a ladderlike impression in the sand. Early morning and evening shadows make these tracks easy to see. The sidewinder makes a perfect "J" with its head and a crossed "t" with the tail. All you have to do is follow the J's and t's.

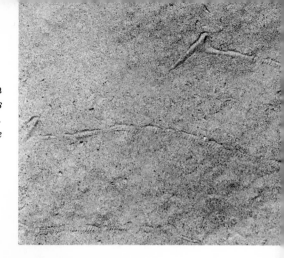

The deadly sidewinder signs its signature on the desert sand. The perfect crossed "t" is made with the tail, the "J" with the head. Distinct tread marks prove that the snake does not slide but rolls its loops along.

How does the snake move in this curious, unique fashion? Does it really sidewind? Does it loop its body along the ground or does it roll along? A sliding automobile wheel does not leave tread marks of the tire. It must roll to leave tread marks. In the snake track, the tread marks are quite distinct. In addition to the head and tail prints, there are the minute crossbars made by the transverse belly scales.

It is evident that the sidewinder does roll along very much like a wheel, only it rolls one loop after another. Once this is understood, the explanation for its great speed becomes clear. Since there is no dragging, much friction is eliminated.

Sidewinder flushed from its hiding place under a bush. As the snake rolls along on its loops it holds as much of itself as possible off the hot sand.

The spade nose snake buries itself in the desert sand with the aid of a long upper jaw with a snout that is flattened for digging.

A few hundred years before Christ, the Greek philosophers said that the greatest pleasure known to man is to learn about the universe. Anyone who has studied the marvelous adaptations made by the animals and plants of the Southwest desert wonderland will agree with those philosophers that the explanations make fascinating stories.

The pits of the pit-viper are located between the eye and the nostril on both sides of the head. They are heat sensitive which makes it possible for the snake to seek out a warm blooded rodent in the dark of the night.

Index

Agave, 38
Alkaline lakes, 14
Annuals, 44
Antelope ground squirrel, 42
Badwater, Death Valley, 14
Bailey's collared lizard, 60
Banded gecko, 55
Barrel cactus, 43
Beetles, 46, 47
Bob cat, 48
Borax, 16
Cactus, 42, 63
Cactus wren, 18
Camels, 28, 29
Cenozoic Era, 27-29
Centipede, 47
Century plant, 38
Chuckwalla, 50, 59
Coati, 13
Coyote pups, 48
Creosote bush, 37, 38
Death Valley, Calif., 9, 10, 14, 16-18, 22,
    24, 25, 36
Deserts, Arabian, 10
    Argentinian, 12
    Atacama, 9, 10, 11
    Australian, 10
    Chihuahuan, 14
    Colorado, 11, 13
    Gobi, 12, 29
    Great Basin, 13
    Libyan, 17
    Mojave, 7, 10, 13-15, 17, 25
    Patagonian, 12
    Sahara, 9, 10
    topographic, 12
    tropical, 10
Dinosaurs, 26
Dry lakes
    Bonneville dry lake, 15
    Muroc dry lake, 15
    Mono Lake, 15

Basins, 35
Dry wash, 20, 39
Duckbilled dinosaur, 27
Dust devil, 20
Eagles, 56
Edwards Air Force Base, 15
Egypt, 9
Erosion, 22-24
Flash floods, 20, 39
Fossils, 25,26
    fish, 26
    giant ferns, 26
    key, 25
    marine invertebrates, 25
    trilobites, 25
Geology, 25
Gilamonster, 56
Gila woodpecker, 43
Great Salt Lake, Utah, 14
Harvester ants, 51
Hawks, 56
Heat, 17
    capacity, 17
    conductivity, 17
Horned lizard, 58
Horses, 28-31
Horse latitude, 14, 21
Humboldt Current, 10
Indians, 30, 35, 36
Joshua tree, 24, 40, 41
Kangaroo rat, 51, 54
Kit fox, 9, 48
La Brea Tar Pits, 27, 28
Las Vegas, Nev., 7, 18
Le Conte Thrasher, 46
Libya, 9, 24
Lichens, 32
Lizards, 53-58
Los Angeles County Museum, 29, 31
Mesozoic Era, 26, 27
Mesquite, 35-37
Minerals, 16

Mirages, 18
Mistletoe, 35, 37
Mono Lake, Calif., 15
Mormons, 30, 41
Oasis, 19
Ocotillo, 16, 42
Paleontology, 25
Paleozoic Era, 25, 26
Palm Springs, Calif., 7, 18, 34
Palm tree, 33-35
Paloverde, 40
Phainopepla, 35, 37
Photosynthesis, 32, 50
Pioneers, 30
Plant succession, 33
Protoplasm, 17
Pyramid Lake, Nev., 14, 15
Quail, 45, 46
Roadrunner, 18, 49, 56
Saguaro, 43, 44
Salt pan, 15
Salton Sea, Calif., 14, 24
San Andreas fault, 34

Sand dunes, 23
  barchans, 24
  Coachella Valley, 24
  life in, 50-52
  Stovepipe Wells, 24
Santanas, 20, 21
Scorpion, 47, 52
Sidewinder, 57, 61
Sirocco, 22
Smoke tree, 39-41
Tarantula, 47
Tortoise, 57
Walking-sticks, 50
White sands of New Mexico, 23
Wind
  chinook, 21
  compression, 20
  foehn, 21
  harmattan, 21
  khamsin, 22
  sirocco, 22
  trade, 10, 12, 21, 22
  tropical, 20
Yucca, 40

NORMAN HAMMOND WAKEMAN

has had an interest in sea life since boyhood. A native Californian, he grew up exploring the coastal rocks and wildlife. He majored in biology and chemistry at Stanford University. In connection with his teaching, which has included science at Pasadena City College, he became an expert wildlife photographer and lecturer, contributing to the Walt Disney *True Life Adventures* and to the films of the Moody Institute of Science, and the television shows, *Bold Journey, Disneyland, I Search for Adventure, George Pierrot Presents, Michigan Bell Telephone Show* and the *Mutual of Omaha Show*.

In studying the creatures that make their homes on the tidal shelf, Mr. Wakeman constantly takes field trips to see and photograph the varied forms of life in their natural habitat.

Norman Wakeman and his wife, Deborah, a graduate of Scripps College, and their three children, Bill, Jim and Caroline, live at the edge of the sea, on an island in a harbor at Newport Beach in Southern California. Many summers have been spent sailing adjacent waters and to the Channel Islands, thirty miles off shore, exploring and photographing. One summer the family lived aboard a thirty-foot sailing ship. Other vacations have been spent traveling by car and house trailer along the sea coast from Mexico to Canada.